C000240874

THE JOURNEY

The Crystal Lake

Part Three of The Journey

Written by
Hilary Jane Jones

Design and Photography by
Tracey Swain

Briar Ridge Books

First published in 2017 by Briar Ridge Books
Whittingslow, Church Stretton, Shropshire SY6 6PZ

A CIP catalogue record for this book is available from
The British Library.

Printed and bound in the UK by

Gomer Press, Llandysul, Ceredigion

ISBN: 978-0-9572371-3-1

www.briarridgebooks.co.uk

1 3 5 7 9 10 8 6 4 2

Cover image: Bwlch Nant yr Arian Forest Visitor Centre
Nr. Aberystwyth, Wales

This book is dedicated to everyone,

young and old, who loves to wander,

loves to dream ...

Never let reality chain your imagination:

Mother Nature is full of wonder

and surprise.

Welcome to Part Three of The Journey

Let your imagination travel beyond the deceptively beautiful crystal lake, through the haunted vale ... to the Mountains of Eternity that lie at The Journey's end.

The faerie glen lay far away,

Day turned to night and night to day,

Then gliding down we watched day break,

Paint gold dust on a crystal lake.

Its sparkling promise mesmerised,

Its lost horizon drew my eyes.

"Your journey must continue on

'til heaven and earth appear as one."

Alone, alongside waters deep,

The world around me stirred from sleep,

Sinister, ruthless, down they came,

Determined to pursue their game.

Others watched from verdant shores:

Kneeling, I begged, “No more, no more!

Leave me to journey on in peace,

Pray let this persecution cease”.

From skies above, a whispered plea:

“Arise, come quickly, follow me!

’cross shimmering waters lies our way,

Where sirens bathe and sunbeams play.”

Across the lake a path appeared,

My trail to tread, escape from here:

"Belief and trust need always be

Within your heart to set you free".

Faith took my hand, walked by my side,

My strength, my saviour and my guide,

But oh! one fleeting moment's doubt:

My path was lost; now no way out!

Stranded! Was nowhere safe to tread?

One ill-judged step, I'd soon be dead:

Watchful and wary my advance,

Through tangled weed I took my chance.

Fate helped when I could take no more:

’til finally I neared the shore,

“Come, come, whilst hope and dreams survive,

This watery grave you’ll leave, alive”.

Along the water's edge I crept,

Past tangled roots where spirits slept,

Each step I took 'twas plain to see

Both good and evil watching me.

Look! Hiding, waiting, coiled and calm:

Did it mean me help or harm?

One poisonous strike, one fatal kiss,

The old man would have dealt with this.

So oft into my thoughts he strayed,

A shadow where no sunlight played:

His omens gave me strength and power,

Brought solace in my darkest hour ...

I wished that he was here ... but no,

The wicked wood would not let go:

Sometimes I wondered if he knew

The perils that I journeyed through ...

"Take care", he'd warned, "for what you see

May not be what it seems to be:

Look but don't touch, walk calmly past,

Yet know each step may be your last ...

Oft in great beauty danger lies,

Death is a master of disguise,

She'll reach for you - you won't resist

The sweetness of her deadly kiss".

From darkened skies Thor's thunder crashed,

Clouds fought and fled, barbed lightning flashed,

Treacherous torrents tumbled, roared,

Spirits fled and dragons soared.

The swollen lake engulfed the land,

Serpents prowled the path I'd planned.

On hands and knees I scrambled past,

Frightened, shaking, crawling fast.

Two days, two nights, afraid to sleep,

Alongside swirling waters deep:

Escape lay where wild waters wailed,

Dark watchful eyes of those who'd failed.

At last a place to lay my head,

Warm earth bestowed a welcome bed:

Mischief and magic came to play,

Brightened my dreams, foretold my way ...

"Follow the water as it climbs,

Leave not its course at any time;

Its ancient rocks must be your guide,

Your shelter should you need to hide".

Far, far into the wood I strode,

A deepening gorge my crooked road,

Timeless secrets lingered long:

Misty whispers, perfumed song.

Deep in my heart lay constant fear,

How would I journey on from here?

Never too far from watchful eyes:

Danger looked on in deft disguise.

Breathless, I climbed, I ran, I wept:

Faint, ’neath a rugged crag I slept.

Riding the breeze, sweet fae-folk flew,

Far from the faerie glen they knew ...

“We come to keep you safe from harm,

Bring morning sun to keep you warm,

One final odyssey awaits,

So near, and yet so far, your fate”.

I left the crystal lake behind,

Imprisoned by my troubled mind,

One place alone could set me free,

The Mountains of Eternity.

Few climbed above their lower slopes,

There lay lost dreams, abandoned hopes.

Most stuck to old familiar tracks,

Around they went ... around and back.

Some became spirits caught in time,

Fixed in perpetual pantomime:

No chance to do another take,

Fated to make the same mistakes.

No more for me the wicked wood,

The faerie glen was lost for good,

The crystal lake would soon run dry:

I turned to bid them all goodbye.

Still I must scale the mountain's height,

Wander where stars encircle night,

Journey to realms where dreams are sown,

Seek out a future few have known.

I crossed the rocky ridge with fear,

Wild, wizened witches huddled near,

Venomous curses soured the air:

"Make haste" they cackled, "if you dare!

If you should reach the farthest end

Into the haunted vale descend:

Seldom do folk come out alive,

Only the chosen few survive.

Know that we're never far away,

Our form may change from night to day

Creatures you think are friends and guides

May lead you to the darker side".

All on my own, yet not alone,

Shadowy shapes, half-seen, unknown,

Beneath each rock, behind each tree,

Someone, something watching me ...

Eyes, dark as night, I felt their stare,

Words on the wind, yet no one there,

Moonbeams that flirted with the night

Danced 'ere they met the morning light.

Time was no friend, its passage slow,

Tiredness an ever-present foe,

Truth and imagination merged:

"Stay strong," my faerie guardians urged.

Their voices brought such sweet relief,

As ever, though, my joy was brief:

Black storm clouds raged, as from his throne

The devil rained down jagged stones.

Gusts turned to gales, rain slashed my face,

Fae disappeared without a trace,

Thorn trees, as old as time, swept by,

Sucked from the earth and doomed to die.

Barring my way, sharp golden claws,

Scratching for blood as I stepped forward:

Beautiful, bright ... their sole intent

To lure with soft, seductive scent.

Look! At my feet, what scuttled past?

Tiny and timid, running fast,

Turning to beckon, lure me down

Into a world beneath the ground.

Stumbling, tumbling, falling free,

I followed it - it followed me!

Fingers reached out, we tumbled through,

Falling, falling .... deja vu.

A mossy pillow ’neath my head ...

Was I alive ... or was I dead?

Far I dropped, I knew not where:

A ghostly silence chilled the air.

Though night had ebbed, still grey the sky,

Where'er I looked death met my eye,

And in the stillness, now and then,

The slightest touch ... again, again.

Yet nothing, no one, could I see:

Imagination ... set me free!

It moved! It sneered! That witchy rock!

Deep underground, a frenzied knock ...

Unrest, confusion, everywhere,

A voice arose on frigid air,

"So many try, so many fail ...

Welcome to the haunted vale!"

Laughter bounced from side to side,

Whispered warnings echoed ... died.

The path beneath seemed safe to tread ...

Yet warring clouds fought overhead.

Who to believe ... the earth, the sky?

The valleys low, the hilltops high?

See and be seen ... or hide away?

Trust the night, beware the day?

The path of fate twists through our mind,

Nature can be both cruel and kind:

A precious gift, a bitter foe ...

We each must choose which way we go.

Into a vast unknown I stepped,

Soft, through the haunted vale I crept,

Thunder still rumbled, grumbled, roared,

In fiery skies wild dragons soared ...

I watched in nervous disbelief,

Fear fell away, turned to relief:

They gave me wings, said I could fly,

I rose to join them in their sky

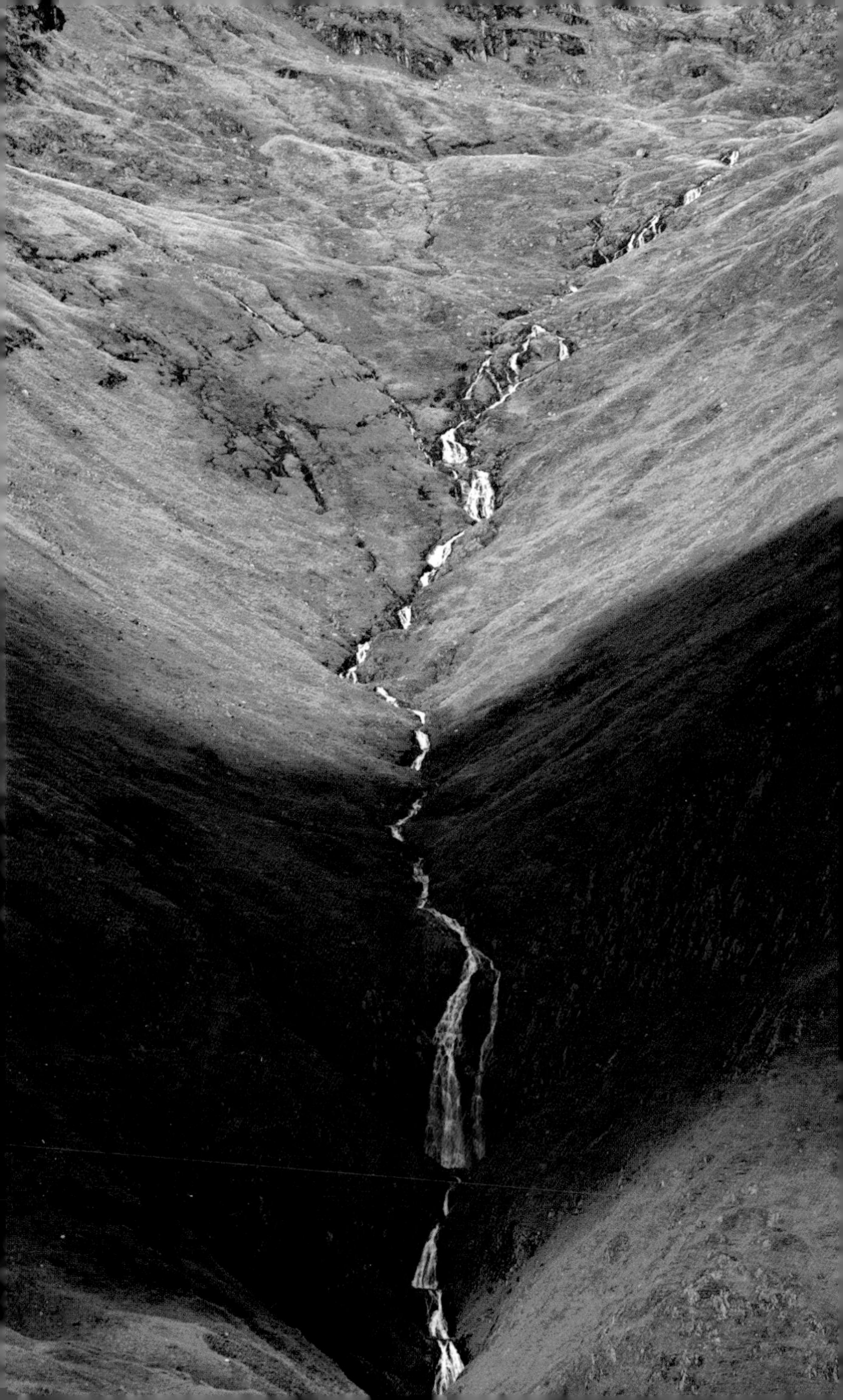

Still witches cast more evil spells,

Forked lightning flashed a path to hell.

My dragons sighed, their fiery breath

Condemned those hags to certain death.

Higher we flew, and far below,

The winding path I'd had to go:

Perilous woods, fierce, thorny trees,

Rocks where I'd crawled on bloodied knees ...

Glens where I'd danced with tiny fae,

Shimmering lakes where sunbeams played.

Daily I'd had a choice to make:

How to react, which path to take.

Others may do it differently,

May never get as far as me.

Now at my journey's end I see

Those Mountains of Eternity ...

Rising into an endless sky,

A universe beyond the eye:

No one can ever, ever know

How far that diamond darkness goes.

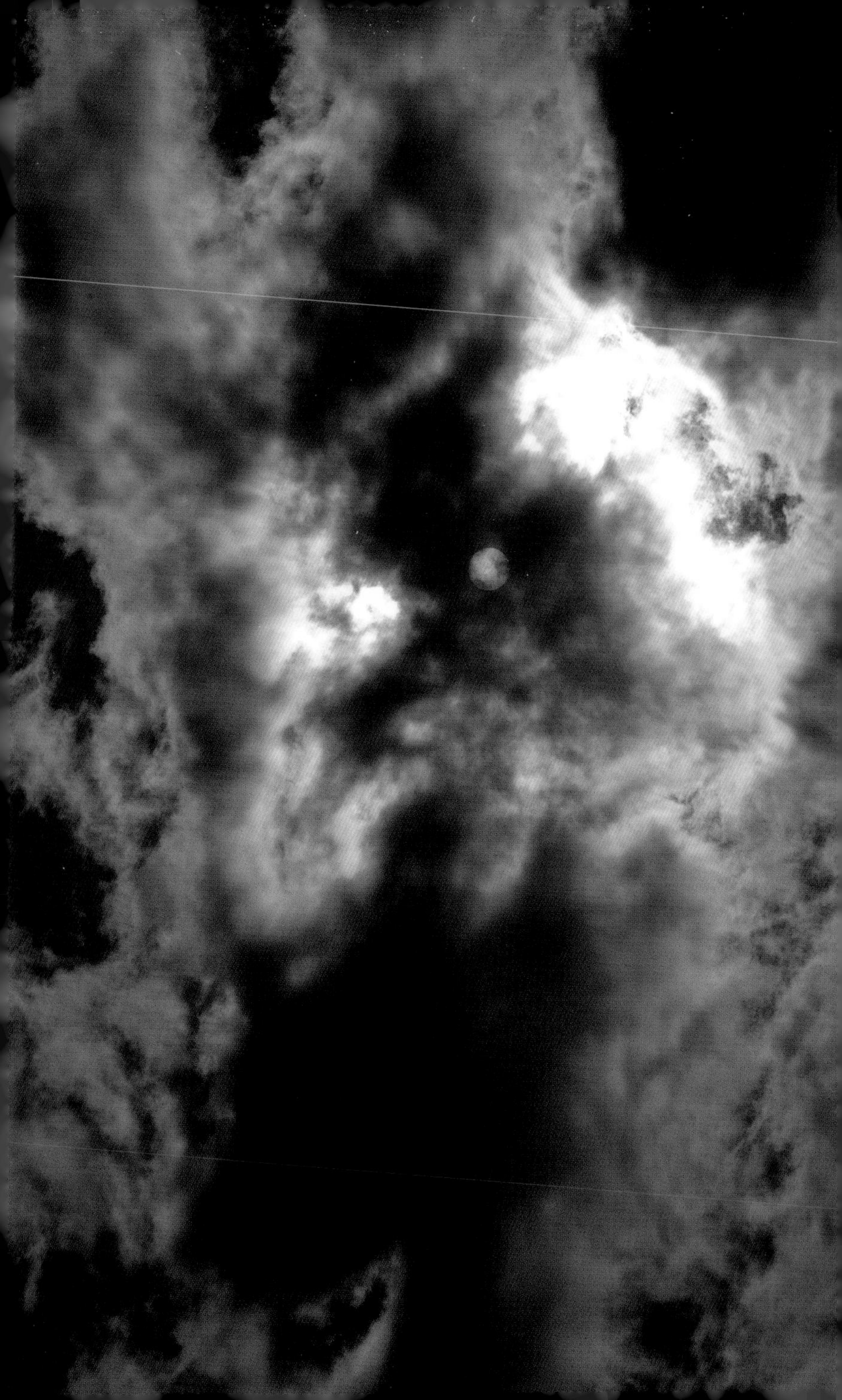

Those who I met along my way,

Maybe I'll find again one day ...

Another life, another place:

Time is the master of my fate.

Still in the distant wicked wood,

Tears in his eyes, the old man stood:

You were my guardian and my guide,

I was your hope, your spirit child.

You cannot ever come with me,

You'll never share my fantasy,

Your eyes don't see what my eyes see:

You have your own reality ...

The End

WHERE OUR JOURNEY BEGAN

The Journey was born from love and respect for the beauty of nature and the countryside in and around Shropshire and the Welsh borders, where magic and mystery so often linger unseen. Hilary and Tracey have woven a fantasy that has captivated hearts and minds across the generations, finally reaching its conclusion in this third book.

Haunting images with hidden secrets.

Reality, or a trick of the eye?

The end ... or a new beginning?

Only you can decide.

In Part One of *The Journey* enter the inner depths of the wicked wood, where dread and fear fill each footstep. Meet the mysterious 'old man' who leads the narrator along the wood's twisted, tortuous tracks, where trees extend claw-like branches, past dens where snakes and spirits hide, through sunshine, snow and rain...

The Wicked Wood is inspired by real landscapes and fertile imaginations. Words and images come together to weave a mysterious and intriguing story that will draw you into a hidden world and make you wonder where *The Journey* is leading.

In Part Two of *The Journey*, join the narrator in the enchanting faerie glen, where all is not what it first appears to be and danger often lurks in cunning disguise. Meet the shy and mysterious fae folk who watch over the narrator now that the old man has disappeared.

Once again, inspired by real landscapes and fertile imaginations, words and images come together to continue a mysterious and intriguing story that will draw you into a hidden world.

The narrator of *The Journey* remains an enigma from beginning to end.

Join us in our secret shire,
44 individual poems and photographs

South Shropshire and the Welsh Borders are home to some of the loveliest scenery in the world. From where the morning sun rises over the rolling Stretton Hills, to where it sets behind the rugged Welsh mountains, there lies a land steeped in beauty and mystery, folklore and history.

Tracey's stunning photography - often described as "painting with light" - is brought to life alongside Hilary's perceptive and imaginative verse.

See latent landscapes emerging, mystical, ethereal figures hidden within nature, dark gothic structures, sunrises, sunsets, misty vales ... and so much more that you may not have realised was there.

Poetess and Painter of Light

Hilary Jane Jones is a writer and poet,
born and bred in Shropshire.

Tracey Swain is a photographer who fell in love with the landscape and light of Shropshire on a short visit and promptly moved there in 2007.

A love of fantasy and a mutual respect for each other's work brought them together to create books that celebrate the landscapes that surround them and at the same time challenge the reader to look a little deeper to see the magic that hides within each scene.

For further information about Briar Ridge Books

briarridgebooks.co.uk

Hilary Jane Jones

hilaryjanejones.net

blogwiththedogs.wordpress.com

Tracey Swain

tnt-photoart.co.uk

elementaltangents.uk